C000070295

PSHE & Citizenship In Action

Year 1

Godfrey Hall

© 2004 Folens Limited, on behalf of the author

United Kingdom: Folens Publishers, Apex Business Centre, Boscombe Road, Dunstable, LU5 4RL
Email: folens@folens.com

Ireland: Folens Publishers, Greenhills Road, Tallaght, Dublin 24
Email: info@folens.ie

Poland: JUKA, ul. Renesansowa 38, Warsaw 01-905

Folens allows photocopying of pages marked 'copiable page' for educational use, providing that this use is within the confines of the purchasing institution. Copiable pages should not be declared in any return in respect of any photocopying licence.

Folens books are protected by international copyright laws. All rights are reserved. The copyright of all materials in this publication, except where otherwise stated, remains the property of the publisher and the author. No part of this publication may be reproduced, stored in a retrieval system, or transmitted, in any form or by any means, for whatever purpose, without the written permission of Folens Limited.

Godfrey Hall hereby asserts his moral right to be identified as the author of this work in accordance with the Copyright, Designs and Patents Act 1988.

Editor: Rebecca Ferguson
Layout artist: Suzanne Ward
Illustrations: Tony Randell
Cover design: Martin Cross

First published 2004 by Folens Limited.

Every effort has been made to contact copyright holders of material used in this book. If any copyright holder has been overlooked, we shall be pleased to make any necessary arrangements.

British Library Cataloguing in Publication Data. A catalogue record for this publication is available from the British Library.

ISBN 1 84303 631 2

Contents

Series introduction

This series has been designed to meet the needs of Key Stages 1 and 2. Prepared in conjunction with the QCA Schemes of Work for Citizenship, it also includes sections on personal, social and health education (PSHE).

Citizenship is a central issue in all schools, and a subject which is part and parcel of our everyday lives. Together with PSHE, it provides pupils with the knowledge, skills and understanding that are required for them to lead happy and confident lives.

It is also important that young people grow up to become not only responsible but also active and informed citizens.

Issues covered in this series include:
- right and wrong
- rules and laws
- fairness
- healthy living
- being part of the community
- decision making
- conflict and cooperation.

The material and ideas in these books have been designed so that they can be used:
- as part of an ongoing programme
- as a springboard for further investigation
- to support existing schemes.

There are 15 units in each book. Each unit contains three sections, each of which focuses on one issue and includes a worksheet to help carry out that task. Each unit provides:
- background information
- learning objectives
- QCA and Curriculum links
- differentiated activities
- follow-up ideas
- three worksheets.

The worksheets have been designed to be flexible and easily adapted to the local needs of schools and individual teachers. The activities have also been designed so that they are cross-curricular.

In the later books, pupils are encouraged to work more and more with outside agencies, extending their knowledge of the subject on both a global and a national level.

Many of the activities throughout the series are excellent starting points for projects within the community as well as for links with other schools.

With the development of e-mail and the Internet, pupils are not only able to communicate with others throughout the world; they are also able to carry out intensive research into areas of interest. This allows schools to build partnerships with others. Pupils also have the chance to work closely with their peers. Working with others, investigating sustainable development and developing local and national strategies are all part of this process.

Citizenship and PSHE are important elements of the curriculum because they:
- encourage pupils to take a full part in the life of the school and the community
- provide pupils with the opportunity to become responsible citizens
- link schools with others elsewhere in the world
- provide the ingredients for a healthy lifestyle
- support and promote equal opportunity and respect
- provide a focus for school-based projects
- provide a chance to work on real-life issues
- increase pupils' decision-making opportunities.

Responding to others

Background

Young children need to learn to become part of a group and work with each other. They must learn to listen to other people's opinions and to voice their own.

Listening is a vital part of the learning process and children should be given the opportunity to develop a range of listening skills. They should be able to co-operate with other people within a group and also be able to listen to them. They should become aware of body language and be able to tell when another child is sad, happy, frustrated or angry.

Learning Objectives

Activities in this unit will allow children to:
- understand the differences between a good listener and a bad listener
- become effective listeners
- know from someone's facial expressions and body language whether they are sad or happy
- practise listening carefully
- understand the importance of communicating clearly.

QCA/Curriculum links: QCA Unit 1 • Worksheet 1 links with English • Worksheet 2 links with English and Art & Design • Worksheet 3 links with English.

ACTIVITIES

Worksheet 1 Listeners

Starting points: Read a short story very quietly to the children. Afterwards, ask them what they remember about it.

Main activity: The children should tick the relevant boxes on the worksheet and then tell a partner why they think the children in the pictures are good or bad listeners.

Simplified activity: The children should complete the worksheet.

Challenge: The children should complete the main activity and then tell their partner what the bad listeners could do to become good listeners.

Worksheet 2 Feelings

Starting points: Show the children some pictures of happy and sad people. Discuss.

Main activity: The children should colour the happy people green and the sad people blue. They can then make up a story to explain what happened to make the people in the pictures happy or sad.

Simplified activity: The children should complete the worksheet. On the back they should draw some of the things which make them happy and things which make them sad.

Challenge: The children should complete the worksheet and go on to discuss what they could do to make a sad person happy.

Worksheet 3 What next?

Starting points: Read a page of a story, then ask the children what they think will happen next.

Main activity: The children should complete the worksheet. The first three events appear to be accidents but the fourth is deliberate. Ask them to talk in small groups about occasions when things like this have happened.

Simplified activity: The children should complete the worksheet and discuss what they would do in these situations.

Challenge: Ask the children to draw a set of four pictures telling a simple story about an accident.

Plenary

- *Tell the children you are going to read a short story and you want them to use their listening skills. At the end of the story, discuss with them what they should have been doing.*
- *Ask the children what makes them happy or sad. Have they ever been involved in an argument? What was it about and what happened?*

PSHE & Citizenship in Action: Year 1

Listeners

 **Are these children good or bad listeners?
Tick the correct boxes.
Colour in the pictures.**

Good ☐ Bad ☐

Good ☐ Bad ☐

Good ☐ Bad ☐

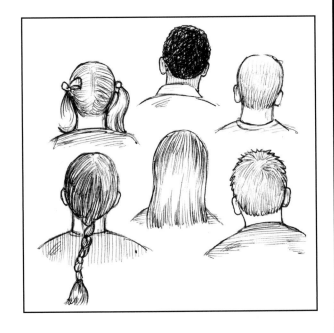

Good ☐ Bad ☐

6

Feelings

Are these children happy or sad?
Colour the happy children green
and the sad ones blue.

What makes you sad?

_____

What makes you happy?

_____

© Folens (copiable page) PSHE & Citizenship in Action: Year 1

What next?

**What would you say if these things happened to you?
Write your answers under the pictures.**

Have you ever had an accident? What happened?

© Folens (copiable page) PSHE & Citizenship in Action: Year 1

② Taking part

Background

Learning how to co-operate and join in are important parts of a child's development. Children need to understand what rules are, why they are needed and when they should be applied. Following rules in the playground and during classroom games are good ways of introducing this subject to young children. They need to know that once rules are agreed they need to be followed.

Learning Objectives

Activities in this unit will allow children to:
- develop an understanding of the importance of rules
- show that they are able to follow different types of rule
- talk about different rules and how they can be applied.

QCA/Curriculum links: QCA Unit 1 • Worksheet 4 links with English and PE • Worksheet 5 links with English and PE • Worksheet 6 links with English.

ACTIVITIES

Worksheet 4 Games

Starting points: Discuss the children's favourite games. Why do they like playing them?

Main activity: The children should complete the worksheet and then draw two more games.

Simplified activity: Ask the children to draw the items that are missing from the pictures on the worksheet and then colour their favourite game.

Challenge: The children should complete the worksheet and then talk about rules they might use every day.

Worksheet 5 Rules

Starting points: Ask the children why rules are important. What happens if they are broken?

Main activity: The children should complete the worksheet identifying waving the bat wildly, picking up the football and leaning on the net as rule breaking, then go on to write down a rule to go with each set of pictures.

Simplified activity: The children should complete the worksheet.

Challenge: Ask the children to play a simple game in a small group and then write down a set of rules for that game.

Worksheet 6 In and out of school

Starting points: Ask the children what the most important rules are at home and at school.

Main activity: The children should complete the worksheet. Ask them to give you some safety rules that should be followed when carrying out each of these activities.

Simplified activity: The children should complete the worksheet.

Challenge: Ask the children to make up some classroom rules. Write them down and put them up on the wall.

Plenary
- *Talk about the importance of having rules. Are there any rules the children use in the playground or at home that could be used in the classroom?*
- *Ask one of the children to show you how they might cross the road. Which set of rules would they use?*
- *Discuss which ground rules should be used in the classroom. Can any of these rules be used in other places as well?*

Games

 **These children are playing games.
Draw in the missing objects.**

football

skipping

cricket

tennis

© Folens (copiable page) PSHE & Citizenship in Action: Year 1

Rules

 Tick the box if the rules are being followed. Put a cross in the box if the rules are being broken.

1.

2.

3.

4.

© Folens (copiable page) PSHE & Citizenship in Action: Year 1

In and out of school

 Which of these would you do at school?
Which would you do at home?
Match the picture with the correct word.

Home

School

School

Home

© Folens (copiable page) PSHE & Citizenship in Action: Year 1

③ Rules

Background

This unit extends the children's understanding of rules by providing a number of practical examples for them to consider. It is important that they realise that they can sometimes discuss and modify rules they have created. The rules of playground games vary from place to place. Hopscotch, for example, has some rules that are constant and others that change around the country. The less formal the game, the more likely it is that there will be different sets of rules in different parts of the UK.

Learning Objectives

Activities in this unit will allow children to:
- take part in setting ground rules
- develop skills of discussion
- respond to others.

QCA/Curriculum links: QCA Unit 1 • Worksheet 7 links with English and Mathematics • Worksheet 8 links with English • Worksheet 9 links with English.

ACTIVITIES

Worksheet 7   Playground games

Starting points: Discuss why the children need rules when they play a game.

Main activity: The children should decide on three rules for each game pictured on the worksheet. They should then explain how each game might be played.

Simplified activity: The children should complete the worksheet.

Challenge: The children should complete the worksheet and go on to discuss in small groups why it is important for everyone to understand the rules before a game starts. What happens if some children play according to a different set of rules?

Worksheet 8   Broken rules

Starting points: Talk about what might happen if a child breaks a rule when playing a game.

Main activity: Ask the children to look at the pictures and circle everyone breaking a rule or law. With a partner, they should think of school rules and what happens when they are broken.

Simplified activity: The children should complete the worksheet and go on to colour the pictures red to show that rules are being broken.

Challenge: Discuss with the children which people try to ensure that everyone keeps to the rules, for example, police officers, teachers, team captains and referees.

Worksheet 9   Class rules

Starting points: Hold up words relating to the classroom, for example 'paint' or 'door'. Ask for a rule connected with each word.

Main activity: The children should complete the worksheet and then discuss what might happen if the classroom rules were broken.

Simplified activity: The children should complete the worksheet, thinking of rules that are easy to follow.

Challenge: The children should draw pictures of children breaking one or more of the class rules.

Plenary

Ask the children to sit in a circle. Quote a rule. Ask each child to say what might happen to them if the rule were broken. What kinds of safety rule should there be inside the classroom and outside in the playground? Why are these so important? Ask the children to tell you if they have ever broken a rule and what happened, for example, climbing a fence and falling off or running in school and bumping into somebody.

Playground games

 Write down three rules for each game.

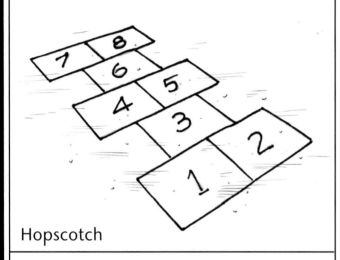

Hopscotch

1. _____

2. _____

3. _____

Chase

1. _____

2. _____

3. _____

Ring-a-ring-a-roses

1. _____

2. _____

3. _____

© Folens (copiable page) PSHE & Citizenship in Action: Year 1

Broken rules

 Circle the people breaking rules or laws.

What might happen to the people who have broken the rules and laws?

_____

_____

_____

_____

© Folens (copiable page) PSHE & Citizenship in Action: Year 1

Class rules

 Write down five classroom rules.

1. _____

_____

2. _____

_____

3. _____

_____

4. _____

_____

5. _____

_____

© Folens (copiable page) PSHE & Citizenship in Action: Year 1

(4) Choices

Background

Children are constantly required to make choices. Doing so requires some skill and expertise. They need to understand and use words linked with choices and be able to make decisions for themselves. This unit provides them with a selection of topics and chances to make choices either on their own or in groups.

Learning Objectives

Activities in this unit will allow children to:

- recognise that, as individuals, they can make their own choices
- share their choices with others
- explain their own choices and look at alternatives.

QCA/Curriculum links: QCA Unit 2 • Worksheet 10 links with English and Science • Worksheet 11 links with English, Art & Design and Geography • Worksheet 12 links with English and Science.

ACTIVITIES

Worksheet 10 — Food

Starting points: Sit the children in a circle and ask each in turn to name their favourite food. Go round again and ask for favourite drinks.

Main activity: The children should complete the worksheet and then talk about what else they might eat and drink at each of these meals.

Simplified activity: The children should complete the worksheet.

Challenge: The children should complete the worksheet and then go on to discuss healthy options for each meal.

Worksheet 11 — Play

Starting points: Discuss the safest place to cross the road near the school.

Main activity: Ask the children to draw a picture showing somewhere safe where they play.

Simplified activity: The children should complete the worksheet and then tell a partner why the places they have ticked are safe.

Challenge: In small groups, the children should talk about what is important when they are choosing a safe place to play.

Worksheet 12 — What to wear

Starting points: Ask the children to bring in a favourite piece of clothing. In a group, ask them to say why they like it.

Main activity: Discuss with the children the importance of having different clothing for different types of weather.

Simplified activity: The children should complete the worksheet. Ask them to talk to a partner about the kinds of clothes they wear for school and when they go out to play.

Challenge: The children should investigate different types of material and find out which are waterproof.

Plenary

Bring in a puppet and ask the children to make a number of choices on its behalf. Discuss how certain things might influence someone's choice. Talk about why it is sometimes hard to make a choice. Working in pairs, ask the children to try to persuade their partner to change a choice, for example, to wear a woolly hat on a hot day.

Food

**Look at these foods.
Choose one for each meal.
Join the food to the meal.**

Breakfast

Lunch

Dinner

What do you eat for breakfast?

_____

© Folens (copiable page) PSHE & Citizenship in Action: Year 1

Play

**Look at the pictures below.
Tick the ones which show safe places to play.
Why are those places safe?**

Underline the safest places to play.

1. In a park.

2. On the road.

3. In a playground.

4. On a railway line.

5. Near a pond.

6. In your garden.

© Folens (copiable page) PSHE & Citizenship in Action: Year 1

What to wear

**Look at the weather.
Circle the clothes the child should wear.**

**Which are your favourite clothes?
Why do you like them?**

_____

_____

© Folens (copiable page) PSHE & Citizenship in Action: Year 1

⑤ Influences

Background

When someone makes a choice they can be influenced by other people and by circumstances. Children may be persuaded to do something by friends, teachers, relatives or other people. They may also be influenced by a change in circumstances, for example, they may decide to change their clothes because of a change in the weather. Children are also affected by advertising. They should understand why people make certain choices.

Learning Objectives

Activities in this unit will allow children to:
- gain experience of making their own decisions
- understand that other people or circumstances may affect a decision
- make decisions and choices based on a set of facts.

QCA/Curriculum links: QCA Unit 2 • Worksheet 13 links with English and Mathematics • Worksheet 14 links with English • Worksheet 15 links with English and Art & Design.

ACTIVITIES

Worksheet 13 Television programmes

Starting points: Make a chart to show the children's favourite television programme.

Main activity: The children should complete the worksheet. Discuss with them how decisions are made in their home on what television programmes to watch. Who has the last word?

Simplified activity: The children should complete the worksheet and tell a partner why they made their choice.

Challenge: In small groups, ask the children to think of television adverts they can remember. Ask them to act some of these out or describe them. Have they ever bought something they have seen in an advert?

Worksheet 14 Who might help?

Starting points: Discuss how the children decide what they are going to wear.

Main activity: The children should complete the worksheet and then discuss why they might change their mind about what to wear outside.

Simplified activity: The children should complete the worksheet. Which people in each list might persuade them to change their mind or even make the decision for them?

Challenge: The children should complete the worksheet and then go on to draw on the back the person who has the greatest influence over their choices, for example, an older sister or a good friend.

Worksheet 15 You have a choice

Starting points: Discuss what the children enjoy doing after school.

Main activity: The children should add an extra option to each of the activities on the worksheet, then complete it and discuss the choices they have made.

Simplified activity: The children should complete the worksheet.

Challenge: Ask the children to imagine that they are holding a party. They should write out or draw a list of food and drink they would like. They could also list games they would like to play.

Plenary

Discuss who can influence the children's decisions.

Ask the children to work in pairs. Give them some decisions to make, for example, 'Which would be the best colour for a new classroom carpet?' Give them the opportunity to discuss their choices with their partner. Have they ever made a mistake when choosing something, for example, it was the wrong colour or they didn't like the taste?

Television programmes

 Colour in the type of programme you would choose.
Why did you make that choice?

Who chooses the programmes you watch?

© Folens (copiable page) PSHE & Citizenship in Action: Year 1

Who might help?

 Tick the person who is most likely to help you to choose.

What to eat?

brother or sister ☐

police officer ☐

just me ☐

doctor ☐

What to wear?

teacher ☐

mother ☐

pet ☐

bus driver ☐

What to play?

friend ☐

teacher ☐

nurse ☐

just me ☐

© Folens (copiable page) PSHE & Citizenship in Action: Year 1

You have a choice

What do you think these people would choose and why?

An old lady on her way to the shops.

- Bus

- Taxi

- Bicycle

Mum or dad just home from work.

- Read a newspaper

- Watch the television

- Get a meal

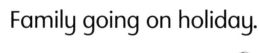

Family going on holiday.

- Camping

- Seaside

- Farm

On the back of this sheet, draw a picture showing what you would choose to wear for a party.

24

© Folens (copiable page) PSHE & Citizenship in Action: Year 1

⑥ Likes and dislikes

Background

This unit deals with children's likes and dislikes. It recognises that everyone is different and everyone has different opinions. It examines a variety of likes and dislikes and goes on to investigate the reasons for the children's decisions.

Learning Objectives

Activities in this unit will allow children to:
- discuss what they like and dislike
- understand that other people may disagree with them
- understand that other people do not have to like the things they like.

QCA/Curriculum links: QCA Unit 2 • Worksheet 16 links with English • Worksheet 17 links with English, Science, Design & Technology and History • Worksheet 18 links with English and Geography.

ACTIVITIES

Worksheet 16 — Like or dislike

Starting points: Ask the children each to name something they like and something they dislike.

Main activity: The children should complete the worksheet, focusing on their preferences in foods, colours, drinks or animals

Simplified activity: The children should complete the worksheet, drawing or writing things they like and dislike.

Challenge: The children should complete the main activity and go on to explain to a partner why they have made specific choices.

Worksheet 17 — Clothes

Starting points: Show the children pictures from a clothes catalogue. Which do they like or dislike? Why?

Main activity: In small groups, ask the children to talk about the kinds of clothes they like and don't like wearing. They should cut pictures from magazines showing clothes they like and clothes they dislike.

Simplified activity: The children should complete the worksheet.

Challenge: The children should complete the main activity and go on to explain to a partner what appeals to them about the clothes they like, for example, colour, material or style.

Worksheet 18 — Places to go

Starting points: Talk about holidays. Bring in some postcards and holiday snaps.

Main activity: The children should complete the worksheet and go on to discuss in small groups where they would like to go on holiday and why.

Simplified activity: The children should complete the worksheet.

Challenge: The children should examine holiday brochures, cut out pictures of places they would like to visit and stick them onto a large piece of paper.

Ask them to look at each other's choices and find the similarities and differences.

Plenary

- *Sit the children in a circle and then ask each of them to name things they like and things they dislike. To extend this, ask them to explain the reasons behind their decisions. Then choose a topic and repeat the exercise. Ask the children to choose someone they know and list their likes and dislikes. For example, 'What does your mum like to eat or wear?' 'What is her favourite colour?'*
- *Make some labels showing the names of different foods or colours. Hold each one up and ask the children who likes each one, and who dislikes it. Put a chart on the wall showing how many children liked it and how many disliked it.*

Like or dislike

 Fill in the spaces.

I like ...

I don't like ...

© Folens (copiable page) PSHE & Citizenship in Action: Year 1

Clothes

 Colour in the clothes you like.
Add another person wearing clothes you like.

Which clothes do your parents or grandparents wear? Why?

_____

_____

© *Folens (copiable page) PSHE & Citizenship in Action: Year 1*

Places to go

Draw a picture in each box.

Seaside	Jungle
Farm	Under the sea

Where would you like to go on holiday?

© Folens (copiable page) PSHE & Citizenship in Action: Year 1

7 Meals

Background

This unit allows the children to think about why they make choices and helps them to discuss personal experiences. It concentrates on a subject they are familiar with – meal times. They will have an opportunity to think about factors that may influence a choice or decision and to reflect upon alternatives.

Learning Objectives

Activities in this unit will allow children to:
- consider factors in their decision making
- understand that there are sometimes alternatives.
- discuss their own experiences.

QCA/Curriculum links: QCA Unit 3 • Worksheet 19 links with English and Science • Worksheet 20 links with English and Science • Worksheet 21 links with English and Science.

ACTIVITIES

Worksheet 19 What to use?

Starting points: Discuss a possible menu for lunch or an evening meal.

Main activity: The children should complete the worksheet and tell a partner what they would use to eat each meal and why.

Simplified activity: The children should complete the worksheet.

Challenge: The children should complete the worksheet. In small groups they should discuss possible alternatives to their suggestions.

Worksheet 20 Where?

Starting points: Show some pictures of different foods. Ask the children which ones they think are healthy. Which ones are bad for their teeth?

Main activity: The children should complete the worksheet, writing down where they eat each meal and adding information about who eats with them. Where do they like eating best? Who do they like to eat with?

Simplified activity: The children should complete the worksheet, drawing the place where they eat each meal.

Challenge: The children should complete the main activity, adding why they eat in these places.

Worksheet 21 Choosing

Starting points: Bring in empty food packets. What was inside them? When would the children eat that food?

Main activity: The children should complete the worksheet. Discuss why they have made their choices.

Simplified activity: The children should complete the worksheet.

Challenge: Ask the children to prepare some imaginary meals using pictures, toy food or junk modelling equipment and set them up on a table in the classroom.

Plenary

- *Discuss with the children which kinds of utensil are needed to eat different foods. Pass a piece of cutlery around a circle. When you say, 'Stop!' the person holding it should name something they could eat with it, for example, if they are given a spoon they could choose soup or jelly.*
- *Ask the children to make up some different meal menus using foods and drink shown on Worksheet 21 or choose one item from the worksheet and ask the children to name something you might eat or drink with it, for example, egg and bacon, tomatoes and lettuce.*

29

What to use

Put these meals in the correct order

Tea   _____

Dinner   _____

Breakfast   _____

Lunch   _____

Match these with the correct food or drink.

   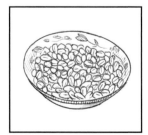

Which do you use for breakfast and which for dinner?

© Folens (copiable page) PSHE & Citizenship in Action: Year 1

Where?

 Draw a picture to show where you eat each of these meals:

Breakfast

Lunch

Dinner

Who eats with you?

© Folens (copiable page) PSHE & Citizenship in Action: Year 1

Choosing

 **Look at the food and drink.
Circle and colour the things you like.**

When would you eat your... breakfast, lunch, dinner?

© Folens (copiable page) PSHE & Citizenship in Action: Year 1

Right and wrong

Background

This unit allows the children to consider situations and decide for themselves whether something is right or wrong. They will decide what the right choice would be and what the wrong choice would be – which situations are safe and which unsafe. These activities can be extended to include a variety of other situations. The children can also be asked to give advice to someone, for example, 'I wouldn't do that because...' With more able children, discuss other issues relating to right and wrong, for example, 'Is it wrong to hit someone or call them names?'

Learning Objectives

Activities in this unit will allow children to:
- understand the difference between right and wrong
- consider alternatives
- discuss issues of right and wrong with others.

QCA/Curriculum links: QCA Unit 2 • Worksheet 22 links with English, Mathematics, Science, Geography and Art & Design • Worksheet 23 links with English and Art & Design • Worksheet 24 links with English and Science.

ACTIVITIES

Worksheet 22 Road safety

Starting points: Ask one child to dress in bright clothes and one in dark clothes. Which would be most visible at night?

Main activity: Discuss with the children the things that people wear to be seen clearly, for example, bright colours, reflective bands or strips.

Simplified activity: The children should complete the worksheet and colour in the pictures.

Challenge: Ask the children to list or draw safe places to cross the road around the school. What has been done, if anything, to slow traffic down?

Worksheet 23 Stranger danger

Starting points: Discuss why it is unwise to talk to strangers.

Main activity: The children should draw up a list of people they think are not strangers. Talk to them about the list and discuss the people they have chosen.

Simplified activity: The children should complete the worksheet. Discuss with them the importance of saying, 'No!'

Challenge: Ask the children to make up a short play about saying 'No!'

Worksheet 24 Home dangers

Starting points: Show a picture of the inside of a home and discuss possible dangers.

Main activity: The children should complete the worksheet and talk about how these dangers could be avoided.

Simplified activity: The children should complete the worksheet.

Challenge: The children should carry out a safety check in the classroom. Are there any dangers? If there are, what can be done about them?

Plenary

- *Sit in a circle and talk about the difference between right and wrong. Go round, giving every child a chance to speak. Read out some sentences relating to safety and ask the children if each is right or wrong.*
- *Sing 'London's Burning' and then talk about why it was right to fetch the fire engine and the water. What might someone have done wrong that started the fire?*

PSHE & Citizenship in Action: Year 1

Road safety

 Write underneath the pictures if these are safe or unsafe places to cross the road.

_____

_____

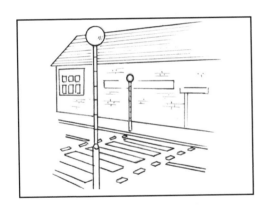

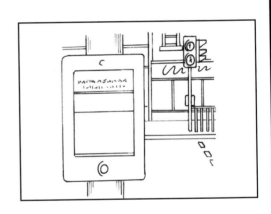

_____

_____

_____

_____

What can you wear so drivers can see you clearly?

© Folens (copiable page) PSHE & Citizenship in Action: Year 1

Stranger danger

 A stranger is someone you don't really know. Remember, if a stranger asks you to go with them:
Run-Yell-Tell
Draw a picture of a stranger below.

© Folens (copiable page) PSHE & Citizenship in Action: Year 1

Home dangers

**Look at the picture.
Circle any things that are dangerous.**

© Folens (copiable page) PSHE & Citizenship in Action: Year 1

(9) Problem solving

Background

This unit gives the children opportunities to look at some problems and decide how they might solve them. This would be a good time to discuss with them what they should do if they see something happening which demands immediate action. Discuss the emergency services and look at what each service does. Contact one of the services and ask a representative to come to talk to the children about their job, for example, a fire-fighter, police officer or paramedic.

Learning Objectives

Activities in this unit will allow children to:
- practise using their problem-solving skills
- consider other children's point of view
- learn how to make a 999 call.

QCA/Curriculum links: QCA Unit 1 • Worksheet 25 links with English • Worksheet 26 links with English, Science and Design & Technology • Worksheet 27 links with English, Mathematics, Science and Design & Technology.

ACTIVITIES

Worksheet 25 Emergency

Starting points: Look at a selection of pictures of the police, fire brigade, ambulance and coastguard service. Discuss what they do.

Main activity: The children should complete the worksheet, drawing and writing the name of the person they would call. Explain how to make a 999 call and the importance of not misusing the system.

Simplified activity: The children should complete the worksheet and, on the back, draw the people they would call.

Challenge: The children should make up a play about an emergency and how they save the day.

Worksheet 26 Solve it

Starting points: Write some simple problems on cards and ask the children to think of possible solutions.

Main activity: Ask the children to make up some problems and then ask a partner to show how they would try to solve them, using role play.

Simplified activity: The children should complete the worksheet. Give them some other simple problems to solve, for example, how would they move a heavy object?

Challenge: Discuss with the children ways in which an older brother, sister or known adult might be able to help if there is a problem.

Worksheet 27 Alternatives

Starting points: Write on card some games or activities. Ask the children to suggest alternatives.

Main activity: The children should complete the worksheet, suggesting as many ways as they can of getting off the island. For example, the boy could light a fire, make a raft or make a flag to wave.

Simplified activity: The children should complete the worksheet, suggesting one or two ways of getting off the island.

Challenge: In pairs, ask one child to tell the other about a problem and then ask them for a possible solution. For example, what would they do if they could not remove the top from their drink? Ask them to work together to decide on the best solution.

Plenary

Give the children some examples of problems that might occur during a day, for example, the alarm clock fails to go off and they oversleep or the electricity goes off and the family cannot cook anything. This can be extended to a practical activity in which they have to work in pairs to solve a simple problem.

Emergency

 Decide who you would call if you saw these things happen.

_____

_____

_____

_____

Which number do you dial in an emergency?

_____

© Folens (copiable page) PSHE & Citizenship in Action: Year 1

Solve it

What would you need to solve these problems?
Match them up.

© Folens (copiable page) PSHE & Citizenship in Action: Year 1

Alternatives

 **How would you solve this problem?
How could he get off the Island?**

_____

_____

_____

_____

_____

_____

How many coconuts can you see in the picture?

_____

© Folens (copiable page) PSHE & Citizenship in Action: Year 1

(10) Needs

Background

It is important that children understand that, as humans, we all have basic needs and that we also have certain responsibilities to animals whether they are pets, working animals or wild creatures. The children need to realise that their behaviour can affect the welfare of these creatures.

The activities in this unit build on the early learning goals. While the worksheets are aimed at Year 1 children, they can easily be adapted for use with older students.

Learning Objectives

Activities in this unit will allow children to:
■ understand that humans and animals all have basic needs
■ be aware that they have responsibilities to pets for their care and welfare
■ think about the needs of their pets.

QCA/Curriculum links: QCA Unit 3 • Worksheet 28 links with English and Science • Worksheet 29 links with English and Science • Worksheet 30 links with English, Mathematics and Science.

ACTIVITIES

Worksheet 28 Keeping alive

Starting points: Describe what humans need to keep them alive in the desert and in the freezing cold.

Main activity: The children should complete the worksheet and go on to draw and write on the other side of the sheet any things they think humans need.

Simplified activity: The children should complete the worksheet, matching the words and the needs.

Challenge: Discuss with the children what animals need and whether humans need the same things, for example, food, water and shelter.

Worksheet 29 Keeping pets healthy

Starting points: Show pictures of pets and wild animals. Ask the children to sort them into groups.

Main activity: The children should complete the worksheet and then write or draw on the back some of the things that are needed by both humans and animals to keep them alive and provide them with a happy life.

Simplified activity: The children should complete the worksheet, matching the pet with the food it needs in order to keep it healthy. Ask the children to draw on the back what they think the animal might eat if it lived in the wild.

Challenge: The children should complete the main activity. Ask them to think of differences between the needs of humans and pets.

Worksheet 30 Needs of pets

Starting points: Make a chart to show which pets the children have at home.

Main activity: The children should complete the worksheet and list on the back ways in which they could make life better for one of the pets shown.

Simplified activity: The children should complete the worksheet and colour in the pictures.

Challenge: The children should extend the work in the starting points. What are the pets and where are they kept? Help them to produce a wall chart to show their results.

Plenary

In a circle, ask the children to talk in some detail about their pets and how they look after them. Cut out pictures of several different types of animal. Ask a child to pick one at random and then ask the class to say what its needs might be. Suitable creatures could include a crocodile, hippopotamus, elephant, giraffe or whale. They should decide which creature they like the best.

Keeping alive

 Colour the things we need to keep us fit and healthy. Connect them to their names.

family and friends

home

clothes

water

food

© Folens (copiable page) PSHE & Citizenship in Action: Year 1

Keeping pets healthy

Can you find the missing pet food in the picture?
Match the pet with the food.

© Folens (copiable page) *PSHE & Citizenship in Action: Year 1*

Needs of pets

Why would the pets need the objects in the picture?
Match each pet with one thing it needs.

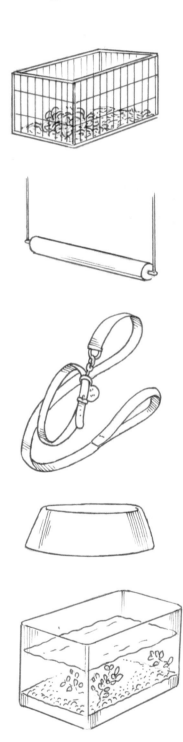

© Folens (copiable page) PSHE & Citizenship in Action: Year 1

(11) People who help us

Background

Children come into contact with lots of adults every day. Many of these people are a major part of their lives. Adults provide help for them during the day, after school and in case of emergency. The children need to recognise who these people are and understand that they are there to help. This unit provides the children with a chance to get to know these people better. They include teachers, school helpers, school crossing patrol officers, police, paramedics and fire-fighters.

Learning Objectives

Activities in this unit will allow children to:
- learn more about the jobs different people carry out
- understand that some people who help them wear uniforms
- know when and who to ask for help.

QCA/Curriculum links: QCA Unit 4 • Worksheet 31 links with English • Worksheet 32 links with English • Worksheet 33 links with English.

ACTIVITIES

Worksheet 31 People who help us

Starting points: Discuss the kinds of job people do at school. Make a list.

Main activity: The children should complete the worksheet. Ask them to write or draw on the back of the sheet some of the things each person needs to carry out their job.

Simplified activity: The children should complete the worksheet and colour the pictures. Help them to read the job titles.

Challenge: In a small group, the children should make up a story involving some or all of these people and turn it into a short play.

Worksheet 32 How do they help?

Starting points: Ask the children to role play different jobs.

Main activity: The children should complete the worksheet and then think about what kind of special clothes these people wear and why. They should draw some of these clothes on the back of the sheet

Simplified activity: The children should complete the worksheet, finding the right person from Worksheet 31 to help. There may be more than one person who can help. Talk to them about what these people might do when they arrive.

Challenge: The children should complete the main activity and then discuss why these people wear special clothes and how the clothes help them with their jobs.

Worksheet 33 Where do these people work?

Starting points: Discuss places of work with the children.

Main activity: The children should complete the worksheet and then on the back draw or write down what each person does when they are at work.

Simplified activity: The children should complete the worksheet and colour the pictures. Talk about other people who might work in the buildings.

Challenge: The children should produce a display showing some of the people who help them in their daily lives.

Plenary

Talk to the children about how the people in this unit help us. What might happen if they suddenly disappeared? How would we cope? How many people can the children think of who have to wear a uniform for work, for example, bus drivers, security guards and nurses. What skills do these people need to have?

People who help us

Match the job with the person.

fire-fighter   ***school patrol crossing officer***

police officer   ***paramedic***

doctor

© Folens (copiable page) PSHE & Citizenship in Action: Year 1

How do they help?

 Look at the pictures below. With the help of Worksheet 31, decide who can help.

Jo   Jim   Brenda   Pat   Lisa

© Folens (copiable page) PSHE & Citizenship in Action: Year 1

Where do these people work?

 Draw the people in the correct places of work.

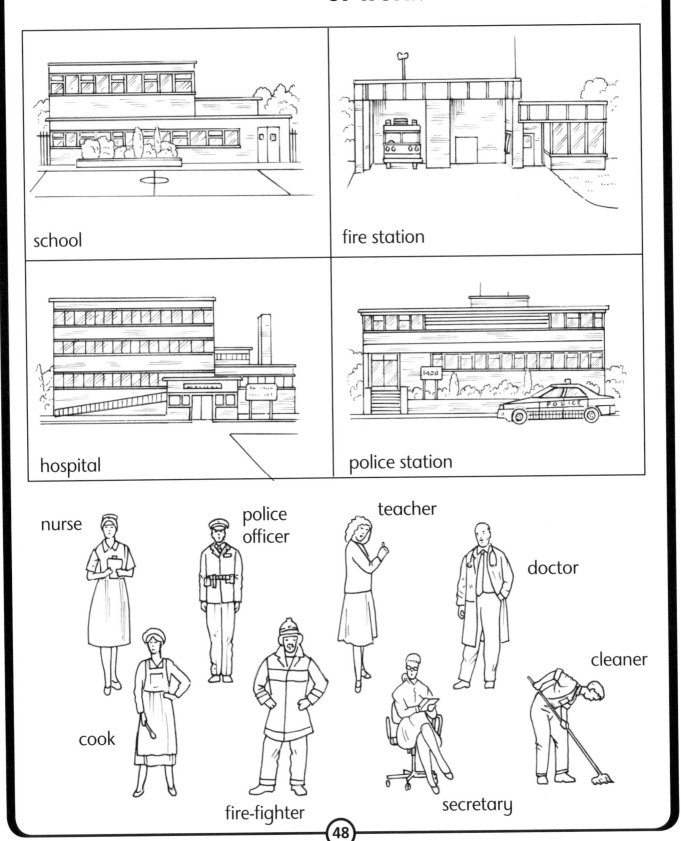

school

fire station

hospital

police station

nurse

police officer

teacher

doctor

cook

fire-fighter

secretary

cleaner

© Folens (copiable page) PSHE & Citizenship in Action: Year 1

999

Background

The children may come into contact with the police in a number of different contexts, for example, they may have to ask for help or they may see a police officer at school. It is important that the children understand what the police do and explore how they operate locally. It is important that the children are aware of the role of the police in relation to crime reduction and help for victims.

Learning Objectives

Activities in this unit will allow children to:
- learn what a police officer looks like and that they wear a uniform
- discuss what police officers do
- know that police officers can be approached for help
- learn when to make a 999 call.

QCA/Curriculum links: QCA Unit 4 • Worksheet 34 links with English and Art & Design • Worksheet 35 links with English • Worksheet 36 links with English.

ACTIVITIES

Worksheet 34 — Police officer

Starting points: Ask the children if they have ever met a police officer. When and where?

Main activity: The children should complete the worksheet, and on the back of the sheet they should draw or write about some of the things a police officer does.

Simplified activity: The children should complete the worksheet, drawing a police officer taking part in an activity.

Challenge: The children should make a police officer's hat out of card and then act out some of the things a police officer does.

Worksheet 35 — Police

Starting points: Make up a song about the work of the police to the tune of 'Old MacDonald'.

Main activity: The children should complete the worksheet, listing ten words linked with the police.

Simplified activity: The children should complete the worksheet and colour in the pictures.

Challenge: The children should cut pictures from magazines and use them to make up a scene showing the police at work. Help the children to write a letter to a local police officer asking if they would be prepared to come in and talk to the class about their job.

Worksheet 36 — Dial 999

Starting points: Bring in a phone and let the children make imaginary 999 calls.

Main activity: The children should complete the worksheet and then write down what is happening in each picture.

Simplified activity: The children should number and colour the pictures.

Challenge: The children should make up a play about an emergency which involves dialling 999.

Plenary
- *Talk to the children about the job of the police. Name an emergency and ask what the children think might happen if they rang 999. Prepare some questions that they could ask a police officer about their job. Arrange for a local officer to come to talk to the children.*
- *Discuss with the children how they can keep their property safe at school.*

49

Police officer

**Draw a picture of your local police officer.
What do they do?**

© *Folens (copiable page) PSHE & Citizenship in Action: Year 1*

Police

Fill in the missing letters.

Police ____fficer

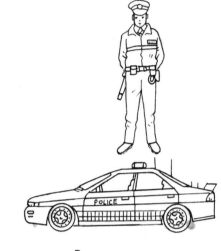

Police ____ar

Police ____an

Police ____og

Police ____ation

Write down some other words to do with the police.

_____

_____

© Folens (copiable page) PSHE & Citizenship in Action: Year 1

Dial 999

**Number these pictures in order.
Write down what is happening.**

_____

_____

_____

_____

© Folens (copiable page) PSHE & Citizenship in Action: Year 1

Similarities and differences

Background

This unit helps children to understand that all of us belong to different groups and cultures, that we all have basic needs and that we live in a very diverse society. They should begin to learn that different things make us the way we are, for example, physical characteristics, friends and culture.

Learning Objectives

Activities in this unit will allow children to:
- recognise and respect the fact that we all have similarities and differences
- understand that we all have basic needs
- understand that we are all special.

Children need opportunities to talk about these issues and to realise that each of them is very special. This work can be reinforced by circle time activities including the chance to say why they and others in the group are special, stressing the value of each element.

QCA/Curriculum links: QCA Unit 5 • Worksheet 37 links with English, History and Geography • Worksheet 38 links with English and Art & Design • Worksheet 39 links with English and Geography.

ACTIVITIES

Worksheet 37 — Similarities and differences

Starting points: Talk about the similarities between people.

Main activity: The children should complete the worksheet and write down what they think is special about each person, for example, curly hair or glasses

Simplified activity: The children should colour in the worksheet, circling what they think is special about each person.

Challenge: Discuss with the children the needs of the four people shown. Ask them to write or draw some of these needs on the back of the sheet.

Worksheet 38 — Differences

Starting points: Discuss ways in which people may differ.

Main activity: The children should complete the worksheet. On the back they should list similarities between the four people shown.

Simplified activity: The children should complete the worksheet.

Challenge: The children should complete the worksheet. On the back, they should draw two people who are complete opposites. Talk with the children about people who are different from each other.

Worksheet 39 — Poco's village

Starting points: Show pictures of a different country. How might life be different there?

Main activity: In small groups, the children should decide what the basic needs are of Poco and his family. Would the children like to live in the village? What reasons can they give for their answer?

Simplified activity: The children should complete the worksheet. On the back they should draw things Poco needs to stay alive and have a comfortable life.

Challenge: The children should use reference books or ICT to find pictures of villages in different countries. Why do the people in the pictures live together?

Plenary

Sit the children in a circle and ask each of them if they can tell you something special about the person sitting next to them. When you have been round everyone, talk about the fact that there are similarities between us all as well as differences. Then talk about our basic needs such as water, shelter and food. A basic need is something required by everyone. Ask the children to name other things which make life more enjoyable.

Similarities and differences

 What is special about these people?

_____

_____

_____

_____

© Folens (copiable page) PSHE & Citizenship in Action: Year 1

Differences

Complete these drawings.

How are these people different from each other?

_____

_____

_____

_____

© Folens (copiable page) PSHE & Citizenship in Action: Year 1

Poco's village

 **How many animals and birds can you find
in this picture?
Circle them.**

What does Poco need to help him have a happy life?

_____

_____

_____

_____

© Folens (copiable page) PSHE & Citizenship in Action: Year 1

(14) Clothes

Background

Taking a theme such as clothes, food or toys, the children can investigate interdependence. They may investigate the sorts of clothes worn by members of the class and then look at clothes worn by people who live in other countries. Children may have parents or grandparents who would be willing to come in and show traditional clothes from their country of origin. It is important that children begin to understand the diversity of races in the UK, understanding that it is important to respect people of all cultures.

Learning Objectives

Activities in this unit will allow children to:
- understand that people from other countries may wear clothes that differ from theirs
- experience different clothes
- appreciate why people may wear different clothes, for example, climatic conditions or religious reasons.

QCA/Curriculum links: QCA Unit 5 • Worksheet 40 links with English and Science • Worksheet 41 links with English and Science • Worksheet 42 links with English and Geography.

ACTIVITIES

Worksheet 40 Clothes

Starting points: Ask the children to explain why they like certain clothes.

Main activity: The children should complete the worksheet and draw a picture on the back showing a set of clothes they like to wear.

Simplified activity: The children should complete the worksheet and then colour in the clothes they like the best.

Challenge: Talk with the children about when they might wear the clothes shown and why. They could bring in an example of something they like to wear.

Worksheet 41 What shall I wear?

Starting points: Discuss things which affect the clothes people wear.

Main activity: The children should complete the worksheet, then draw up a list of five friends and the clothes they like to wear.

Simplified activity: The children should complete the worksheet, colouring in the clothes they have chosen.

Challenge: Show the children a selection of pictures from magazines showing people wearing different clothes. Ask why they think those people choose to wear those clothes.

Worksheet 42 Who are we?

Starting points: Discuss why some people have to wear special clothes for their job.

Main activity: The children should complete the worksheet. On the back of the worksheet they should give each child a different name and a different choice of clothing.

Simplified activity: The children should name and colour the children on the worksheet. Discuss with them why they made their selection.

Challenge: The children should use the labels on a selection of clothing to investigate where each item was made.

Plenary

Show the children a number of items of clothing from different cultures. Pass each item round. Explain what it is and ask the children if they might wear it. Discuss their answers. Emphasise that clothes can be worn by anybody, but sometimes they have to be worn for a particular reason. It is important to avoid stereotyping and generalisations and to show that some people wear modern clothes while others choose to wear traditional items.

Clothes

 **Look at the clothes below.
Tick the things you like wearing.**

Why do you like wearing these?

_____

_____

© Folens (copiable page) *PSHE & Citizenship in Action: Year 1*

What shall I wear?

 **Choose some clothes for this girl.
Colour them, cut them out and stick them on.**

© Folens (copiable page) PSHE & Citizenship in Action: Year 1

Who are we?

**Look at the pictures below.
Give each child a name.**

**What kind of clothes do you think they like wearing?
Where do you think their clothes were made?**

_____

_____

60

(15) Our school

Background

The focus in this unit is on the school. The children could walk round the school and try to think of things that could be changed to make it a more friendly and welcoming place. Areas to look at include the playground, inside the building and the area in front of the school. Other year groups can be successfully involved in this work. Year 1 and 2 could work together and identify a project to work on together. In this way the children will have the opportunity to discuss issues with children and adults outside their own class.

Learning Objectives

Activities in this unit will allow children to:
- take part in discussions with children outside their own class
- contribute to the life of the school
- work together as a group.

QCA/Curriculum links: QCA Unit 6 • Worksheet 43 links with English and Mathematics and Geography • Worksheet 44 links with English • Worksheet 45 links with English.

ACTIVITIES

Worksheet 43 A better place

Starting points: Discuss how a day at school might be improved.

Main activity: These children should complete the worksheet. Discuss with them how their own school might be improved.

Simplified activity: These children should complete the worksheet, drawing on the back some of the ways in which they might improve the school in the picture.

Challenge: These children should complete the worksheet and then list on the back ways in which they could improve their own classroom.

Worksheet 44 The playground

Starting points: Ask the children to name things at school that make them happy.

Main activity: The children should complete the worksheet and list on the back things that make them feel happy or sad in the classroom.

Simplified activity: The children should complete the worksheet. Discuss with them things which make them happy or sad in the playground. Help them to write their ideas down.

Challenge: The children should complete the worksheet and then discuss things which might make other children and adults feel happy or sad in the playground.

Worksheet 45 What can we do?

Starting points: Discuss why the school might need to be changed.

Main activity: The children should complete the worksheet, listing their improvements under their picture. Ask them to explain to a partner why these changes would improve things.

Simplified activity: The children should complete the worksheet.

Challenge: The children should complete the worksheet. Ask them to discuss people who might be able to help with these improvements and then produce a list of possible helpers.

Plenary

Ask the children to sit in a circle. Talk to them about ways in which they might be able to improve the classroom. Are there any practical things they could do? Invite the caretaker or site manager to talk about whether or not their suggestions are practical. Make a list of improvements that might be made and put them on the wall so that other children and adults can see them.

PSHE & Citizenship in Action: Year 1

A better place

 **How could you make this school a
better place?**

_____

_____

_____

_____

_____

_____

© Folens (copiable page) PSHE & Citizenship in Action: Year 1

The playground

 What makes you feel happy in the playground?
What makes you feel sad?

Happy

Sad

© Folens (copiable page) PSHE & Citizenship in Action: Year 1

What can we do?

☞ **Draw a picture to show what you could do to make your classroom or school a better place.**

© Folens (copiable page) PSHE & Citizenship in Action: Year 1